CONTINUED OVER

BUSTER'S Diary

I wanted to watch a wild animal film on TV.

MRS. SNOOT AT No. 13 HAS SPRAINED HER ANKLE AND WOULD LIKE YOU TO TAKE HER PRIZE DOG FOR ITS EXERCISE, BUSTER!

OH DRAT!

OH WELL! THAT *LITTLE* DOG WON'T NEED MUCH EXERCISE! I'LL SOON RUSH HIM ROUND THE BLOCK!

BUT...

THIS IS THE DOG TO BE EXERCISED! KEEP HIM CLEAN, HE'S GOING INTO A DOG SHOW TOMORROW!

WOW! I CAN'T STOP HIM! SLOW DOWN!

WUFF!

I called to some of my pals to help...

HELP ME CONTROL THIS GREAT LUMP, CHAPS!

HANG ON! HE'S SLOWING DOWN!

SNAP!

9

HE'S DISAPPEARED! AND THAT'S WHAT WE'RE GOING TO DO!

WE'VE HAD ENOUGH! YOU'D BETTER TRY CALLING HIM BACK, BUSTER!

OH LUMME! I DON'T KNOW HIS NAME!

So I started to call out all the dogs' names I could think of...

FIDO! CAESAR! SLOBBER CHOPS! PRINCE! WHISKERS! TOWSER! POOCH! RUFF!

I soon got results! All the stray dogs in the district answered my calls...

SOMEONE CALLED MY NAME!

WOOF!

OO! HELP!

PLAYMATES! I'LL JOIN IN!

YAP! YAP!

WOOOF!

WUFF!

Much later, I returned the lady's prize pooch...

WAG!

HE'S HAD PLENTY OF EXERCISE, MISSUS!

OH, NO! WHAT A STATE!

13

And then I returned home... FAST!

AH! YOU'RE BACK IN TIME TO WATCH THE WILD ANIMAL FILM, BUSTER! SHALL I SWITCH IT ON?

13

DOGS DISH

NO THANKS! I'VE HAD ENOUGH WILD ANIMALS!

I had, too! After that I wouldn't let one anywhere near the house!

STOP THAT, BUSTER!

SHOO!

WE MUST BE KIND TO OUR DUMB FRIENDS! I'LL TAKE HIM INDOORS AND GIVE HIM A FEED!

HERE'S YOUR LUNCH, BUSTER, AND SOMETHING FOR THE POOR DOGGIE! TUCK IN!

But the dog tucked into my grub...

HO!!

SCOFF!

THE POOR LITTLE THING MUST HAVE BEEN VERY HUNGRY!

SO AM I NOW!

So, later, I bought some smashing cream buns...

YUM!! YUM! I'LL SOON GET RID OF THIS LOT!

BAKER

CIRCUS

HI! I DON'T WANT ANY HELP TO EAT 'EM!

THERE'S ANOTHER DUMB ANIMAL COMING, MUM!

THEN I MUST FIND SOMETHING FOR THE POOR LITTLE THING TO EAT!

DON'T BOTHER, MUM! THE POOR LITTLE THING WILL FIND SOMETHING HIMSELF!

PANTRY

HE'S EATING ALL OUR FOOD! STOP HIM!

I'LL STOP HIM EATING THESE CREAM CAKES... BY SCOFFING THEM QUICKLY MYSELF! I'M NOT DUMB!

CHOMP!! SCOFF!

OUT!

CAREFUL, MUM! WE MUST BE KIND TO OUR DUMB FRIENDS, YOU SAID!

THANKS FOR FEEDING JUMBO, LADY! HE WON'T WANT ANY GRUB FOR A WEEK, BY THE LOOK OF HIM!

HAVE A COUPLE OF FREE TICKETS FOR THE CIRCUS, AND THESE CHOCOLATES WITH THE MANAGER'S COMPLIMENTS!

CHOCS

So Mum enjoyed watching the dumb animals perform their tricks...

...while I performed a disappearing trick with the chocs!

YUM! MUNCH.

CHOCS

13

IVOR LOTT and TONY BROKE

HELPFUL HETTIE

Bertie Bumpkin

IT'S ABOUT TOIME OI BOUGHT A NEW HAT— THIS OLD UN'S JUST ABOUT 'AD IT!

OI'D LIKE A NEW 'AT, PLEASE!

YES, SIR. HOW ABOUT THIS STYLE— ONLY £3.50?

OI'LL TAKE IT!

THANK YOU, SIR!

HEH, HEH! LOOK AT OLD BERTIE IN THAT NEW 'AT— HE LOOKS A ROIGHT OLD NANA! HEH, HEH!

PERHAPS OI SHOULD 'AVE KEPT ME OLD 'UN, AFTER ALL!

OOPS!

SPLOP

OI! WATCH OUT FOR ME HAT!

FACEACHE

AT BELMONTE SCHOOL

SCRUNGE

BELMONTE SCHOOL'S NEAREST NEIGHBOUR WAS COLONEL GRAPESHOTT OF TOTTERING TOWERS, AND HE HATED BOTH PUPILS AND TEACHERS.

HELLO! COLONEL GRAPESHOTT HERE! BRING THAT BLACKGUARD OF A HEADMASTER THRASHBOTTOM TO THE PHONE!

THIS IS THRASH-BOTTOM SPEAKING. WHAT DO YOU WANT, COLONEL?

GUR! I'VE HAD ANOTHER WINDOW BROKEN BY THOSE DELINQUENT BRATS OF YOURS! IF I CATCH ANY OF 'EM ON MY PROPERTY OVER CHRISTMAS, I'LL HORSEWHIP THE LITTLE BLIGHTAHS, IS THAT CLEAR?

GULP! ER... YES, COLONEL! BUT DON'T WORRY, THEY WON'T BE BOTHERING YOU OVER CHRISTMAS! WE'RE SNOWED UP HERE AND NONE OF MY PUPILS CAN GET OUT!

HUH! AND NEITHER CAN OUR CHRISTMAS GOODIES GET IN! I'M OFF NOW, TO BREAK THE NEWS TO THE KIDS!

BOYS! I REGRET TO SAY THAT, AS THE SCHOOL'S CUT OFF FROM THE VILLAGE BY SNOW, THE GENERAL STORE CAN'T DELIVER OUR YULETIDE PROVISIONS! IT'LL BE A CHRISTMAS DINNER, OF COCOA, AND JAM BUTTIES!

IF THE GENERAL STORE CAN'T GET THROUGH TO US, HOW ABOUT ONE OF US GETTING THROUGH TO THEM – AND BRINGING BACK THE GOODIES?

SOME OF THE SNOWDRIFTS ARE TEN FEET DEEP! IT'S QUITE IMPOSSIBLE!

WELL! I'M GONNA HAVE A GO! WHO WANTS JAM BUTTIES FOR CHRISTMAS!

18

FACEACHE MADE HIS WAY TO THE SCHOOL PLAYGROUND.

HEE-HEE! IT'LL BE *EASY*-FOR ME! ALL I GOTTA DO IS "SCRUNGE" INTO THE INCREDIBLE MOLE MAN OF MULL AND *TUNNEL* MY WAY TO THE GENERAL STORE *UNDER* THE SNOW!

NOW! LEMME GET MY BEARINGS! I'LL BY-PASS TOTTERING TOWERS ON THE LEFT, THEN IT'LL BE A STRAIGHT RUN INTO BELMONTE VILLAGE!

HERE GOES!

SCRUNGE

HEE-HEE! CHRISTMAS GOODIES, HERE I COME!

DIG-DIG-DIG

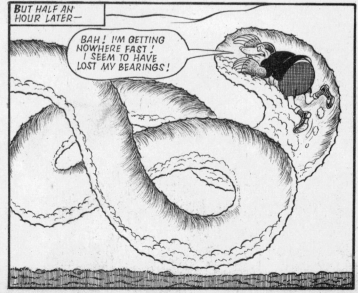

BUT HALF AN HOUR LATER—

BAH! I'M GETTING NOWHERE FAST! I SEEM TO HAVE LOST MY BEARINGS!

OH! NO! NOW, I'VE COME UP AGAINST A STONE WALL! I'LL HAVE TO DIG *UNDER* IT!

MADE IT! NOW TO TUNNEL UP THROUGH THE SNOW AND FIND OUT *EXACTLY* WHERE I AM!

YERK! I'VE BEEN TUNNELING, ABOUT UNDERNEATH TOTTERING TOWERS! I'D BETTER GET *OUT* OF HERE, QUICK!

TOTTERING TOWERS
TRESSPASSERS WILL BE HORSEWHIPPED
COL. GRAPESHOTT. V.C.

AT LEAST I'VE GOT MY BEARINGS NOW! THE VILLAGE IS *THIS* WAY!

AND SHORTLY...

BOY! SUCCESS! I'VE COME UP IN THE GENERAL STORE AND THERE'S THE SCHOOL'S CHRISTMAS ORDER. SOON GET THAT *BACK*!

UN-SCRUNGE

Reno Reno Reno Reno

Belmonte School's XMAS ORDER

BUMP PACK

IT'S AMAZING WHAT YOU CAN ACHIEVE WITH THE RIGHT "SCRUNGE"!

Belmonte School's XMAS ORDER

SHORTLY, IN THE SCHOOL GROUNDS...

YIPPEE! I'M BACK WITH THE GOODIES! NOW TO BREAK THE GOOD NEWS TO OLD THRASH-BOTTOM!

'SCUSE ME, SIR, BUT I GOT THROUGH TO THE VILLAGE. ALL THE XMAS GOODIES ARE IN THE PLAYGROUND!

WELL DONE, LAD! NOW, WE CAN HAVE OUR FEAST!

SO, ON CHRISTMAS DAY....

WELL, BOYS! THANKS TO FACEACHE WE'RE GOING TO HAVE A MERRY CHRISTMAS AFTER ALL, SO I PROPOSE A TOAST TO —

RUMBLE

WHAT THE—

?

GREAT SCOTT! THE MAIN TOWER OF COLONEL GRAPESHOTT'S RESIDENCE! IT'S COLLAPSING INTO THE SNOW!

RUMBLE

CRACK

GRIND

OO 'ECK!

R-R-RING — R-R-RING

?

NOW, WHAT?

YOU FIEND, THRASHBOTTOM! YOUR YOUNG HOOLIGANS HAVE DONE IT THIS TIME. THEY'VE UNDERMINED THE MAIN TOWER BY DIGGING UNDERNEATH AND NOW ITS COLLAPSED!

RUBBISH, YOU OLD FOOL! ONLY ONE OF MY PUPILS HAS BEEN OUT! A CHUBBY LITTLE LAD, CALLED FACEACHE! HOW COULD ONE CHUBBY LITTLE LAD WREAK ALL THAT HAVOC?

(GULP!) OO, 'ECK! I HOPE THEY NEVER FIND OUT!

Ken Reid

The small cat with the BIG appetite!

TIME FOR SOME TRUMPET PRACTICE!

BAH! HOW CAN I PRACTICE WITH THOSE KIDS MAKING THAT RACKET WITH THEIR TOY DRUMS?

BANG THUMP

I'LL SEE IF I CAN FIND PEACE TO PRACTICE OUTSIDE!

SUDDENLY...

THE POLICE!

THERE'S BEEN A BANK ROBBERY! BUT THE CROOKS HAVE GOT CLEAN AWAY!

PEEEE PAWW

POLICE

GASP! MY X-RAY SPECS REVEAL THE BANK ROBBER, HIDING INSIDE THAT FAKE PETROL TANKER!

BANK BANK

27

CONSTERNATION STREET

30

THOSE ELECTRIC FIRES SHOULD HELP THAW THE SNOW WHEN IT C-COMES!

HELLO, CORPORATION? COULD YOU SEND A SNOW PLOW AROUND RIGHT AWAY?

JUST WAIT THERE, MATE! IT'LL SNOW ANY MINUTE!

HE MUST BE POTTY! THERE'S NOT A CLOUD IN THE SKY!

THIS LOT WILL KEEP ME WARM IN CASE HELP'S A LONG TIME COMING!

AND WE'RE HAPPY TO REPORT THE WARMEST WINTER'S DAY FOR 25 YEARS!

WHAT?

YIPPEE! MY FORESIGHT WAS WRONG! IT'S A FALSE ALARM!

33

The kids of Stalag 41

MUSCLES MILLER
NIPPER
WINSTON
JUDGE
DINGER BELL

STALAG 41 WAS A SECOND WORLD WAR PRISONER-OF-WAR CAMP FULL OF BRITISH BOYS. THEIR COMMANDANT WAS THE VERY NASTY COLONEL KLAUS VON SCHTINK.

DEEPER, YOU INSOLENT PIG-BOYS! VEN YOU HAF DUG DOWN TEN FEET... DEN YOU CAN FILL IT IN AGAIN. HA, HA, HA!

WE CAN'T GO ON LIKE THIS... OL' STINKY'S MAKING OUR LIVES A MISERY!

JUST AT THAT MOMENT...

THE MAIL VANS!

BAH! DEY HAF SOMETING TO CHEER DEM UP! I VISH I COULD FORBID DEM TO HAF DER MAILS... BUT IT IS AGAINST DER REGULATIONS!

POW MAIL

HURRRAHHHH!

ONE FOR YOU HERE, WINSTON... AND ONE FOR MUSCLES MILLER...!

LISTEN TO ME! I VANT DER PARCELS OPENED IN FRONT OF DER GUARDS! I AM NOT HAFFING YOU SMUGGLE IN DER TOOLS FOR MAKING DER ESCAPES!

NOTHING ILLEGAL IN HERE SCHTINK! SOAP, CHOCOLATE, CAKE, TOFFEE, WRITING PAPER AND STUFF LIKE THAT...!

HMMMM, DER CHOCOLATE AND DER TOFFEES... HOW I VISH SOMEONE VOULD SEND SOME TO ME!

HEY, MY DAD'S SENT ME AN ACTOR'S MAKE-UP KIT! OL' SCHTINK WON'T LET ME KEEP THAT...!

IT COULD COME IN VERY USEFUL, THOUGH, JUDGE... PASS IT BACK DOWN THE LINE BEFORE HE SEES IT!

MAKE UP

PASS IT BACK...

DON'T LET SCHTINK SEE IT...

BANG ON TARGET!

FIRST ONE BACK TO THE HUT... HIDE IT IN JUDGE'S BUNK!

WHEN THE PARCEL INSPECTION ENDED...

AS YOU HAF YOUR OWN FOOD TO EAT.. DER STALAG DINING ROOM VILL REMAIN *CLOSED* FOR DER REST OF DER VEEK! EAT YOUR OWN GRUB!

OUR PARCELS ARE SUPPOSED TO BE EXTRAS!

THAT EVENING, JUDGE LOOKED AT HIS MAKE-UP KIT...

WELL, WE OUGHT TO BE ABLE TO DO *SOMETHING* WITH THIS...BUT WHAT?

I THINK I'VE GOT AN IDEA, JUDGE, BUT WE'LL NEED TO BORROW ONE OF SCHTINK'S UNIFORMS!

AT MIDNIGHT, DINGER AND WINSTON CREPT FROM THE HUT...

CONNECT THE HOSE TO THAT TAP ROUND THE BACK, JUDGE...TURN IT ON WHEN WE YELL.

OKAY, CHAPS.. GOOD LUCK!

OKAY, JUDGE... TURN IT ON!

DANGER KEEP OUT! ELECTRICITY

FIVE MINUTES AFTER THE TAP WAS TURNED ON, THE WATER LEVEL INSIDE THE HUT ROSE TO TOUCH THE ELECTRICAL CONNECTIONS...

SPPPTTTZZZZ! BOOOOM!

TURN OUT DER GUARD! DER LIGHTS HAF FUSED! VATCH DER PRISONERS DO NOT TRY TO MAKE DER ESCAPES!

IN WE GO..!

THIS ONE WILL DO.. LOOKS LIKE HIS SUNDAY BEST!

NICE PAIR OF SPARE BOOTS, TOO!

BUT AS THE LADS EMERGED FROM SCHTINK'S HUT...

DERE ARE TWO OF DER PRISONERS, MEIN COMMANDANT!

HALT! AFTER DEM, FAT HANS, AFTER DEM..!

DINGER AND WINSTON DASHED THROUGH THE FIRST DOOR THEY CAME TO...

LARD LARD
LARD LARD

THEY'VE SEEN US... THEY'RE COMING!

WE'VE HAD IT!

GET SOME OF THIS STUFF, DINGER...WE'VE STILL GOT A CHANCE-SPREAD IT ON THE FLOOR...!

STAND BACK...THEY'RE COMING!

THIS IS WHERE OL' SCHTINK SLIPS UP...I HOPE!

WELCOME, CHAPS...!

HO, HO! NOW THEY'RE IN THE SOUP!

ON, DINGER, COME GET OUT BEFORE THEY FIND THEIR FEET!

MENU BREAD AND WATER

WELL, WE'VE GOT SCHTINK'S BEST UNIFORM AND A BOX OF MAKE-UP PAINTS...WHAT DO WE DO NEXT?

FIND SOMEONE ABOUT VON SCHTINK'S SIZE... LOFTY WILL DO! NOW WE DISGUISE HIM!

COR, THAT'S GOOD...HE'S BEGINNING TO LOOK LIKE OLD SCHTINK!

HE LOOKS WORSE THAN SCHTINK!

'ORRIBLE!

WHEN THE MAKE-UP JOB WAS FINISHED...

I VOS DER BIG TWIT! STOP DER GUFFAWS, YOU BRITISH PIG-BOYS!

PUT THE UNIFORM ON, TOO, LOFTY!

WHEN LOFTY PUT ON SCHTINK'S UNIFORM...

NOW ALL YOU HAVE TO DO IS GO OUT THERE AND ORDER THE GUARDS TO THROW AWAY ALL THAT TRENCH-DIGGING GEAR WE'VE HAD TO USE!

YEAH... THEN WE WON'T HAVE TO DIG ALL THOSE ROTTEN HOLES!

BUT WHAT IF THEY DON'T BELIEVE ME? I'LL GET DONE IF THEY DON'T THINK I'M SCHTINK!

THEY'LL NEVER THINK I'M SCHTINK!

YES, THEY WILL!

YOU LOOK MORE LIKE SCHTINK THAN SCHTINK DOES!

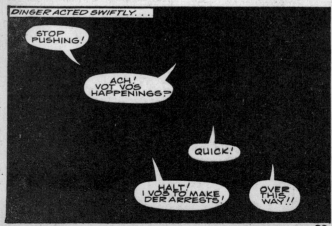

SAY VOT YOU LIKE... BUT I KNOW YOU ARE *NOT* HERR SCHTINK! OUT!

YOU VILL PAY FOR DAT KICK IN DER TROUSERS, FAT HANS!

OKAY, LOFTY... YOU CAN COME OUT! SCHTINK'S GONE!

COR, THAT WAS A CLOSE CALL! I THOUGHT I WAS FOR THE HIGH JUMP...!

LET'S GO AND GET THAT SUPER BREAKFAST YOU ORDERED FOR US, LOFTY!

I'LL STAY BEHIND AND GET THIS GREASE-PAINT WASHED OFF! YOU CAN BRING BACK MY SHARE...!

I'M GOING TO ENJOY THIS LOT!

BEST GRUB WE'VE HAD SINCE WE CAME HERE!

MEANWHILE, FAT HANS HAD MARCHED HIS PRISONER TO THE GUARD HOUSE...

HAF YOU GONE OFF DER ROCKERS, FAT HANS? YOU HAF ARRESTED HERR SCHTINK!

IT IS DER DISGUISES! YOU VILL SEE VEN I VASH IT OFF!

BUT...

IT VOS AMAZING! I SCRUB AND SCRUB AND DER GREASE-PAINT DOESN'T COME OFF!

YOU GREAT OAF, 'HANS...DAT *IS* OUR COMMANDANT! YOU'RE SCRUBBING HIS SKIN OFF!

GRRRRRR!

ARREST HIM AND FLING HIM IN DER CELL!

JA, HERR COMMANDANT, AT VUNCE!

DER BRITISH PIG-BOYS VOS PLAYING DER GAMES, SERGEANT! VE MUST FIND OUT EXACTLY VOT DEY VOS UP TO!

JA, HERR GENUINE SCHTINK! MEIN GOOTNESS VOT TERRIBLE PEOPLE DESE BRITISH BOYS VOS!

WHILE THE BOYS WERE STILL AT BREAKFAST...

HA, HA! DEY VILL THINK DER FLOWERS VOS VERY BEAUTIFUL! ALL DER BRITISH PIG-BOYS LIKE DER FLOWERS! BUT INSIDE IS DER HIDDEN MICROPHONE...FOR ME TO HEAR VOT DEY SAY!

YOU VOS VERY CLEFFER, HERR SCHTINK! EVEN DER GESTAPO COULD NOT THINK UP SUCH A DIRTY TRICK TO PLAY!

NOW, ALL VE HAF TO DO IS LISTEN TO ALL OF DER BRITISH BOYS' PLANS COMING OUT OF DER LOUD-SPEAKER! I AM DER GENIUS!

BUT...

WE BROUGHT YOUR BREAKFAST, LOFTY!

SHHHHHH! SCHTINK'S BEEN IN...HE'S HIDDEN A MIKE IN HERE!

SO THAT'S HIS GAME, EH? WELL, WE'LL SOON FIX THAT!

IN HIS OFFICE, VON SCHTINK WAS LISTENING INTENTLY...

IT VOS HARD TO HEAR, MEIN COMMANDANT! DER BOYS ARE VISPERING...!

PUT DER EARS CLOSER, SERGEANT! IF DEY VISPER IT VOS BECAUSE DEY VOS MAKING DER PLANS! LISTEN HARD...!

ON THE COUNT OF THREE ALL BLOW TOGETHER! ONE...TWO... THREE...!

ARRRRHH... MEIN EARDRUMS!

OWWWWW!

SCREEEEEEEEEDCH!

WE'VE BEEN FOUND OUT, CHAPS, BUT WE GOT SOME LOVELY GRUB!

AND I BET OLD SCHTINK'S WILD!

HE WAS!

ZAT ISS FOR NOT'ING!

THE END

PLAY THE AEROBATIC DOG FIGHT GAME!

ALL YOU NEED IS A DICE, TWO PLAYERS AND TWO COUNTERS

START

ENGLISH SVINEHUND!

WATCH YOUR TAIL, FRITZ!

START

YOUR COUNTERS REPRESENT FIRST WORLD WAR FIGHTER PLANES AND TO START ONE MUST BE PLACED ON THE 'ENGLISH' SIGN AND THE OTHER ON THE 'GERMAN' ONE. TURNS ARE TAKEN TO THROW THE DICE AND THE THROWERS MOVE ACCORDINGLY IN THE DIRECTION OF THE ARROWS—THE BLACK SQUARE GIVES YOU THE CHOICE OF TURNING EITHER RIGHT OR LEFT. WHEN ONE PLANE LANDS ON TOP OF THE OTHER HE HAS SHOT IT DOWN AND SO SCORES A HIT—BOTH PLANES THEN GO BACK TO THE START AND THE GAME CONTINUES TILL ONE PLANE HAS SCORED SIX 'HITS' AND SO BECOMES THE WINNER.

41

43

GASP! I-I DIDN'T MEAN TO PUFF SO HARD! NOW LOOK WHAT I'VE DONE!

KERASH!

BUT...

COR! IT'S RON AND SID LAWLESS, THE JEWEL THIEVES'! THEY'VE JUST FINISHED ANOTHER ROBBERY!

GOOD WORK, BILLY! WE SAW HOW YOU STOPPED THEM!

PHEW! THIS BLOWING LARK'S EARNING ME A LOT OF CASH!

REWARD

ROB LEE

AND SO IT WENT ON...

CLEAR OUR PITCH FOR THE GAME, PLEASE, BILLY!

PUFF!

MY SHEEP ARE BURIED IN THERE, BILLY! HELP ME FIND THEM!

PUFF!

THE PLANES CAN'T LAND UNTIL YOU'VE CLEARED THE RUNWAY, BILLY!

45

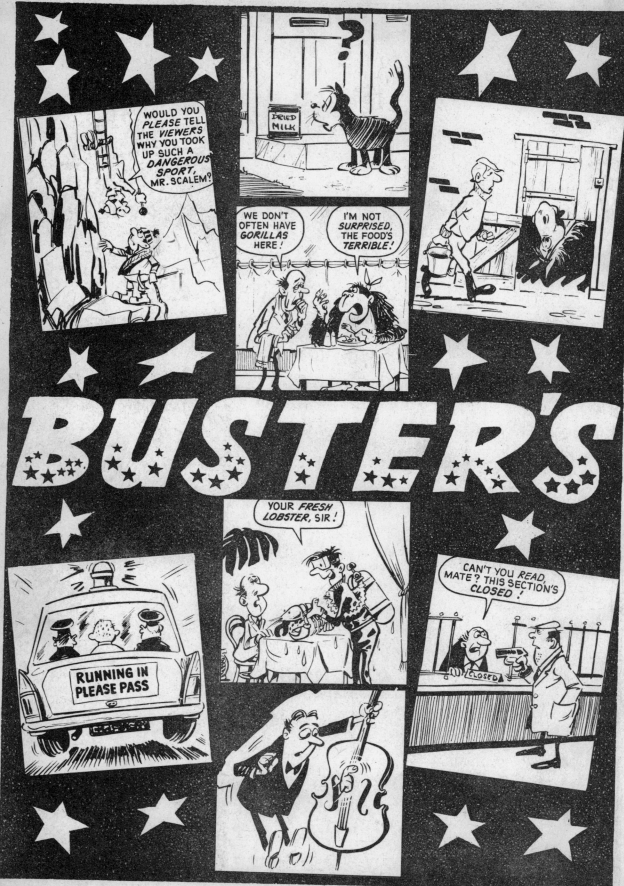

47

FAULTY TOWERS

This is Faulty Towers, oldest school in the land

The old school's so cold in winter, Mr Chipps lets us play games most of the time just to keep warm!

And here **is** Mr Chipps, oldest headmaster in the land!

Boys! Boys! They're back!

Oh, not again!

They are Bigglesworth and Wilkins, two council employees who have been trying for months to knock down the old school...

We won't fail this time, Wilkins! A few swings of our steel ball will knock down that old wreck!

Right as ever, Mr Bigglesworth!

But the pupils like their school so much they don't **want** it knocked down...

After us with a steel ball this time, eh? Right, lads, we'll make some balls of our own!

49

THEY'RE GOING! WE'VE WON AGAIN!

I WOULDN'T BE SO SURE! *THAT'S* NOT THE WAY BACK TO TOWN!

NO... IT'S THE WAY TO UPPLEY MOOR, EVEN HIGHER THAN THE SCHOOL!

THIS'LL FOOL THEM, WILKINS! *WE'LL* SEND A SNOWBALL DOWN ON *THEM*... WITH A *HARD CENTRE!*

OH, REALLY, MR BIGGLESWORTH? AND WHAT DO WE NEED THE STEEL BALL FOR?

DOH! SOMETIMES I THINK YOU'RE THE NEAREST THING TO AN IDIOT!

OOCH! WELL YOU'RE THE ONLY OTHER PERSON NEAR ME, MR BIGGLESWORTH!

BONK!

GET THE IDEA NOW, WILKINS? THEY'LL THINK IT'S A HARMLESS LUMP OF SNOW!

AND IT'LL SMASH THE SCHOOL APART! EE, MR BIGGLESWORTH, HOW *DO* YOU THINK THEM UP?

HO! HO! FAT LOT OF GOOD A SNOWBALL'S GOING TO DO!

HEY! BUT THE BIG BALL'S MISSING FROM THE CRANE!

OH, NO! WE'VE GOT TO STOP THAT THING HITTING THE SCHOOL!

UP THUR

53

Partridge's Patch

ONE OFF-DUTY MORNING, COUNTRY POLICEMAN TOM PARTRIDGE WAS PREPARING FOR THE COMING LOCAL SHEEP-DOG TRIALS...

GET HIM, FELLER! GET!

WHOOOF... WOOOF!

EARLY THE NEXT MORNING....

AH, IT'S GOOD TO BE BACK IN THE **CITY** AGAIN! NO MUD, NO ANIMALS GETTING IN YOUR WAY! EVERYTHING NEAT AND ORGANISED. YOU CAN *KEEP* THE COUNTRY LIFE!

THEN SUDDENLY...

CLAAAANG *CLAAAANG!*

IT'S A *BURGLAR ALARM!* ROUND THAT *CORNER!*

COME ON, FELLER!

THEY'VE RAIDED THAT JEWELLERY SHOP! AND THEY'VE GOT A *CAR!*

GET HIM, FELLER!

WHOOOOOFFF!

FELLER'S TEETH SNAPPED THROUGH ONE CROOK'S COATSLEEVE....

GRRAARR!

UUUUHHH.... GET 'IM OFF...!

NEVER MIND, *NICK!* WE'VE GOT THE STUFF! COME ON... *RUN FOR IT!*

HANDCUFF HIM TO THE LAMP-POST...THEN LET'S GET AFTER THE OTHER TWO.

ALL RIGHT, FELLER! I'VE GOT HIM NOW!

WHICH WAY DID THEY GO?

MAYBE THEY WENT DOWN *HERE!*...AND ARE HIDING IN ONE OF THOSE *SHOP DOORWAYS!*

HOLD IT, INSPECTOR. RECKON YOU BE A MITE WRONG!

SEE. THAT WATER RIGHT ACROSS THE ROAD. IF THEY *HAD* GONE THAT WAY, YOU'D SEE THEIR WET FOOTPRINTS!

I SUPPOSE YOU'RE RIGHT. THEN THEY MUST HAVE GONE INTO THAT *PARK!*

A WEAK, DAZED VOICE GREETED THEM...

TWO MEN...I TRIED TO *STOP* THEM! THEY...THEY *HIT* ME!

ARE YOU HURT, SIR?

58

MARTIN BAXENDALE

DRINKIES, ANGEL!

IS IT POP, MUM?

OH, NO, ANGEL! MUMSIE WOULDN'T GIVE YOU NASTY, GASSY LEMONADE!

I WAS AFRAID SHE WOULDN'T!

I'VE GOT LOVELY ORANGE JUICE, HEALTHY BLACKCURRANT JUICE AND YUMMY ROSE-HIP SYRUP FOR MY LITTLE MAN!

UGH! ALL BABY STUFF!

DRINK IT ALL UP, LAMBKINS! IT'LL DO YOU GOOD!

GLUG GLUG

I MUST BUILD MY LITTLE PET UP TO FACE THE RIGOURS OF WINTER! HE NEEDS ALL THOSE LOVELY VITAMINS!

BLAAAH! A WHOLE WINTER OF THIS! I CAN'T BEAR IT!

BUILD ME UP, EH?... HM!...

PLAN HATCHING

62

CHALKY

ON THE WAY HOME, CHALKY MET HIS PAL CLAUDE...

HEY, CHALKY! I'VE GOT TO MEET MY RICH UNCLE AT THE STATION! COME AND HELP ME LOOK OUT FOR HIM!

OKAY, CLAUDE!

HEH, HEH! HIS UNCLE'S LOADED, IS HE? I'LL GET TO THE STATION AND HELP MYSELF TO SOME OF HIS CASH!

HOW WILL I KNOW WHAT YOUR UNCLE LOOKS LIKE, CLAUDE?

THAT'S EASY! I'VE A PHOTO OF HIM HERE!

HAW, HAW! THANKS, KID! NOW I KNOW WHO TO LOOK FOR!

HUH? WHO ARE YOU?

YIKES! HE LOOKS LIKE A CROOK TO ME! LET'S GET AFTER HIM!

GASP!

STATION

OH, NO! WE'LL NEVER FIND THAT THIEF IN THIS CROWD!

BUFFET

TEE, HEE! WE'LL MAKE HIM FIND US! GET THAT PHOTO OUT WHILE I TURN THIS FIGURE ROUND!

STATION BUFFET

MENU

CHUCKLE! THIS SKETCH WILL BRING THAT CROOK INTO THE OPEN!

WOW! IT LOOKS JUST LIKE MY UNCLE!

AH! THERE HE IS! AND HE'S GOT HIS CASH WITH HIM... THIS'LL BE EASY!

NOW TO GRAB THE CASH AND GET AWAY SMARTLY!

BUFFET

TITTER!

GRR! PINCHING THAT SIGN, EH? YOU'D BETTER COME ALONG WITH ME!

OH, NO!

HI, CLAUDE! NICE OF YOU TO MEET ME!

THAT'S OKAY, UNCLE! WE'VE JUST SEEN SOMEONE OFF AS WELL, THANKS TO CHALKY! CHUCKLE!

BUSTER'S Diary

EMPTY

I wanted to buy Mum a birthday present but my piggy bank was cleaned out.

So I went car cleaning to raise money...

WOULD MR. BLOGGS LIKE ME TO CLEAN HIS CAR, MISSUS?

HE'S NOT AROUND, BUT I'M SURE HE'D BE VERY PLEASED!

So I started...

LIQUID SOAP

JUST WAIT TILL MR. BLOGGS GETS AN EYEFUL OF THIS!

YAAH! I'VE GOT TWO 'EYEFULS' AND A MOUTHFUL! SPLUTTER! CLEAR OFF, YOU NUISANCE!

LUMME! MR. BLOGGS WAS WORKING UNDERNEATH!

Then I tried at the Mayor's house...

WOULD YOU LIKE ME TO CLEAN YOUR CAR, MR. MAYOR?

YES! BUT THERE'S NO TIME! I'VE GOT TO GO TO A MEETING IN FIVE MINUTES — SO HOPPIT!

I'LL DO IT ANYHOW! AT TOP SPEED!

LIQUID SOAP

I'M OFF! GOT TO HURRY!

COR! THIS IS TAKING LONGER THAN I THOUGHT IT WOULD!

LIQUID SOAP

The TRAP

A FAST-MOVING ADVENTURE OF

THUNDERBOLT

The AVENGER

WHO WAS THE MYSTERIOUS THUNDERBOLT? ALWAYS THERE WAS SOMEBODY TRYING TO DISCOVER THE SECRET, BUT NEVER BEFORE HAD THUNDERBOLT BEEN FOLLOWED HOME BY FIGHTER PLANES...

THOSE PILOTS HAVE BEEN SENT TO KEEP AN EYE ON ME... FIND OUT WHO I AM. GOT TO GIVE 'EM THE SLIP SOMEHOW!

AND THERE'S THE ANSWER DOWN THERE... JUST IN TIME! I'VE GOT TEN MINUTES SUPER POWER LEFT!

THUNDERBOLT'S INCREDIBLE WRISTWATCH GAVE HIM TWO HOURS OF SUPERPOWER. AFTER THAT IT TOOK 24 HOURS TO RECHARGE AND DURING THAT TIME HE WOULD REVERT TO AN ORDINARY MAN!

THAT'S THE ANSWER... THE TUNNEL!

A TRAIN!

HE'S GOT TO COME OUT OF THAT TUNNEL SOME TIME. YOU WATCH THE EXIT, I'LL STAY THIS END!

ROGER!

BUT AS THE TRAIN ROARED OUT OF THE TUNNEL...

GOOD! THEY HAVEN'T SPOTTED ME!

RIDING THE BUFFERS, THUNDERBOLT SAVED THE POWER OF HIS WATCH UNTIL THE TRAIN REACHED LONDON...

TIME TO GET OFF... BEFORE I GET PINCHED FOR NOT HAVING A TICKET!

AND THREE MINUTES LATER...

ONE OF THESE DAYS SOMEONE'S GOING TO SEE ME ARRIVE HERE... AND THEN THE GAME WILL BE UP!

AH, THAT'S BETTER... POLICE CONSTABLE MICK RILEY... READY TO REPORT FOR DUTY!

SOME DAYS LATER...

WE'RE TAKING TIGER MALONNI DOWN TO THE TOP SECURITY JAIL THIS MORNING, RILEY... YOU'LL RIDE INSIDE WITH HIM.

SURE THING, SARGE... HE'LL BE SAFE ENOUGH WITH ME.

IF HE TRIES TO ESCAPE... CLOBBER HIM, RILEY. BECAUSE IF HE DOES GET AWAY... I WILL CLOBBER YOU, SEE?

ER, YES, SARGE... RELY ON ME.

74

A FEW MILES FROM THE MAXIMUM SECURITY JAIL...

LISTEN... THE POLICE WAGON'S COMING NOW. YOU KNOW WHAT TO DO?

SURE, BOSS!

SLOW DOWN, PERKINS... YOU CAN'T GET ROUND THAT THING.

FANCY DRIVING IN THE MIDDLE OF THE ROAD LIKE THAT... IT'S DANGEROUS!

IT WAS VERY DANGEROUS... FOR THE POLICEMEN!

THAT GAS SHELL WILL KNOCK 'EM ALL OUT... AN' BY THE TIME THEY COME ROUND, MALONNI WILL HAVE VANISHED!

THE PLAN WORKED PERFECTLY, ONE HOUR LATER MALONNI WAS IN LONDON...

WHY DID YOU RESCUE ME? WHAT DO YOU GET OUT OF IT?

I WANT THUNDERBOLT ...ALIVE! I AIM TO FORCE HIM TO TELL ME THE SECRET OF HIS AMAZING POWER!

YOU'RE AN ESSENTIAL PART OF MY PLAN, MALONNI, THAT'S WHY I RESCUED YOU!

BUT HOW CAN I HELP?

YOU WILL BE BAIT! THUNDERBOLT WILL COME AFTER YOU AS SOON AS HE KNOWS YOU'VE ESCAPED FROM PRISON, AND WHEN HE DOES...

...I'LL BE READY FOR HIM!

75

THE NEXT DAY, CONSTABLE MICK RILEY HEARD THAT MALONNI HAD BEEN SPOTTED NEAR THE RIVER...

THIS IS A JOB FOR THUNDERBOLT!

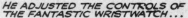

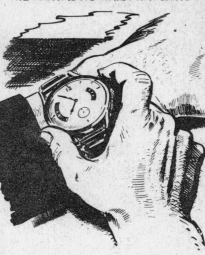

HE ADJUSTED THE CONTROLS OF THE FANTASTIC WRISTWATCH...

AND A SECOND LATER...

OKAY, MALONNI...I'M COMING FOR YOU!

ABOARD A MOTOR-LAUNCH MOORED ON THE THAMES, STOOD MALONNI AND HIS RESCUER...

LOOK! THERE'S THUNDERBOLT!

GOOD! MALONNI...ALL YOU HAVE TO DO IS STAND STILL! AND DON'T FORGET... I WANT THUNDERBOLT TAKEN ALIVE!

HIGH ABOVE THE RIVER, THUNDERBOLT SAW THE LAUNCH SUDDENLY LIT UP BY ITS OWN SEARCHLIGHT...

MALONNI!

BUT AS THE ONE-MAN POLICE FORCE DIVED DOWN

THERE'S SOMETHING WRONG ABOUT ALL THIS! WHY IS MALONNI STANDING THERE FOR EVERYONE TO SEE?

RIGHT INTO MY LITTLE TRAP... LIKE A FLY INTO A SPIDER'S WEB! OKAY, MR. THUNDERBOLT... TAKE THIS!

THE STRANGE-LOOKING GUN JERKED WITH THE RECOIL...

BOOM!

IT WAS NOT A SHELL THAT ERUPTED FROM THE MUZZLE... BUT A STEEL NET!

YOU GOT HIM!

UNDER THE WEIGHT OF THE ENCIRCLING NET...THUNDERBOLT PLUNGED INTO THE WATER...

A TRAP! THEY WERE WAITING FOR ME. MALONNI WAS THE BAIT. AND I FELL FOR IT!

I'M NOT FINISHED YET... NOT BY A LONG WAY!

AAAARHHH!

WHAT ABOUT THUNDERBOLT? HE'LL DROWN IN THAT NET!

LET HIM! SAVE YOURSELF FIRST, MALONNI!

ON THE MUDDY BOTTOM OF THE RIVER...

THEY'LL NEVER HOLD ME WITH THIS THING! IT'LL TAKE MORE THAN A STEEL NET TO OVERCOME THE POWER OF MY WRISTWATCH!

BUT, BY THE TIME THE AVENGER REACHED THE SURFACE...

THEY'VE GOT AWAY! BUT I'LL CATCH UP WITH YOU, MALONNI... AND WITH YOU, MR. DARK-GLASSES WHOEVER YOU ARE!

BUT MALONNI AND HIS MYSTERIOUS FRIEND VANISHED COMPLETELY. AND P.C. MICK RILEY RETURNED TO DUTY AT POOL STREET POLICE STATION...

YOU'LL BE COMING TO THE NEW YEAR FANCY-DRESS BALL TOMORROW, MICK?

OF COURSE HE'LL COME. I CAN JUST SEE HIM NOW...IN HIS LITTLE GNOME'S COSTUME!

YOU SHOULDN'T TEASE P.C. RILEY LIKE THAT, SERGEANT!

WELL, HE'S SUCH A WEAK-KNEED LITTLE NINNY! I DON'T KNOW HOW A WEAKLING LIKE HIM EVER GOT IN THE FORCE! MUST HAVE BEEN A MISTAKE!

THE POLICE FANCY-DRESS BALL WAS ALSO UNDER DISCUSSION IN THE BASEMENT GARAGE OF A BLOCK OF FLATS NOT FAR AWAY...

YOU WANT ME TO GO TO THE POLICE BALL?

YES! WE KNOW THUNDERBOLT DIDN'T DROWN... AND WE KNOW HE HELPS THE POLICE FORCE. IF YOU SHOW YOURSELF AND RUN FOR IT... THUNDERBOLT WON'T BE FAR BEHIND YOU!

I'LL BE OUTSIDE WAITING FOR YOU IN THIS CAR. IT'S SPECIALLY DESIGNED TO CATCH THUNDERBOLT. TWIN-BARRELLED GAS-GUN IN THE BOOT, FIRING AUTOMATICALLY!

IT HAS A FEW OTHER LITTLE TRICKS, TOO!

THAT'S SOME CAR!

ALL P.C. RILEY'S OFF DUTY MOMENTS WERE SPENT SEARCHING FOR MALONNI... AS THUNDERBOLT...

WELL, I'LL HAVE TO GIVE UP SEARCHING FOR TONIGHT. IF I DON'T GO TO THE FANCY-DRESS BALL... SERGEANT MEREDITH WILL HAVE SOMETHING TO SAY!

A FEW MINUTES LATER, THUNDERBOLT ALIGHTED ON THE POLICE STATION ROOF...

NOW TO CHANGE INTO MY GNOME'S OUTFIT! IT'LL GIVE THE SERGEANT A LAUGH, ANYWAY!

AT THAT MOMENT...

OH!

SHE MUST NEVER KNOW P.C. RILEY AND THUNDERBOLT ARE ONE AND THE SAME PERSON. I'LL HAVE TO BLUFF!

HOW-HOW D'YOU LIKE MY FANCY-DRESS OUTFIT, MARY? ORIGINAL, EH?

OH, MICK... FANCY COMING AS THUNDERBOLT! YOU'RE GOING TO HAVE EVERYONE LAUGHING AT YOU. ESPECIALLY THE SERGEANT!

MARY WAS RIGHT!

HA, HA! OLD WEAKLING RILEY IN **THAT** OUTFIT!

ASK HIM TO USE HIS AMAZING STRENGTH TO CRACK A NUT!

THE ONLY FLYING HE COULD DO... IS FLY FOR HELP!

AND IN A CORNER OF THE ROOM... TIGER MALONNI WATCHED...

I'LL SLIP AWAY TO THE OUTER OFFICE AND PUT THE PLAN INTO ACTION!

THE ONLY PERSON IN THE OUTER OFFICE WAS POLICEWOMAN MARY LANDSON... IN HER PARTY OUTFIT.

WHO ARE YOU?

THE MAN THEY'RE ALL LOOKING FOR, MISS. TIGER MALONNI! PUT UP YOUR HANDS... AND KEEP **QUIET**!

FED UP WITH THE LAUGHTER AND JEERS MICK RILEY EDGED OUT OF THE ROOM.

MALONNI!

PUT 'EM UP, COPPER!

YOU COULDN'T BE THE REAL THUNDERBOLT, COULD YOU? JUST PRETENDING TO BE IN FANCY DRESS, EH? I THINK I KNOW HOW TO FIND OUT...

NO, I GUESS YOU'RE JUST AN UNDER-NOURISHED COPPER, AFTER ALL! THUNDERBOLT WOULD NEVER LET ANYONE HIT HIM!

I MUSTN'T FIGHT BACK... I MUSTN'T LET HIM KNOW THE TRUTH!

A MOMENT LATER... IN THE PARTY ROOM...

WHAT WAS THAT?

A GUN! THREE SHOTS! WHAT'S HAPPENING OUT THERE?

SERGEANT MEREDITH LED THE RUSH TO THE DOOR...

RILEY! WHAT'S GOING ON OUT HERE? HOW DID YOU GET IN THAT STATE, YOU IDIOT?

IT—IT WAS MALONNI, SARGE! HE WAS IN HERE... DRESSED AS A JESTER. HE TIED US UP... FIRED THREE SHOTS INTO THE CEILING... AND BUNKED!

AND YOU LET HIM GO! WHY DIDN'T YOU FIGHT HIM, MAN... INSTEAD OF LETTING HIM STUFF YOU IN THE WASTEPAPER BASKET!

OUTSIDE THE POLICE STATION, MALONNI BOUNDED INTO THE CAR WAITING FOR HIM.

IT ALL WORKED SWEETLY, BOSS... JUST AS YOU SAID!

GOOD WORK, MALONNI. SOON THEY'LL BE CHASING US... AND THEN THUNDERBOLT WILL APPEAR ON THE SCENE! WHICH IS JUST WHAT WE WANT!

MALONNI AND THE MYSTERY MAN SPED AWAY... AND SQUAD CARS BEGAN TO CONVERGE UPON THEM...

THEY'RE GAINING ON US, BOSS!

GOOD! THERE'S A LEVER AT THE SIDE OF YOUR SEAT... PULL IT BACK HARD!

AS MALONNI PULLED THE LEVER, THE BOOT OF THE CAR OPENED...

AND NOW TO ELIMINATE THE SQUAD CARS!

A SQUIRT OF FLAME LEAPT FROM THE MUZZLES OF THE TWIN-BARRELLED GUNS AND TWO SMOKE SHELLS HURTLED THROUGH THE AIR...

LOOK OUT!

I CAN'T SEE... WE'RE CRASHING!

BACK AT POOL STREET POLICE STATION, P.C. MICK RILEY MADE HIS WAY UP INTO THE SMALL ATTIC ROOM UNDER THE ROOF...

IT'S TIME THUNDERBOLT TURNED ON THE POWER! I DON'T MIND MALONNI MAKING ME LOOK A FOOL... BUT HE'S NOT GOING TO GET AWAY WITH IT THIS TIME!

CLEAR OF ALL PURSUIT, MALONNI WATCHED THE SKY...

HERE HE COMES, JUST AS YOU SAID, BOSS. IT'S THUNDERBOLT!

SWIFTER THAN A HAWK... STRONGER THAN A TIGER... THUNDERBOLT SWOOPED DOWN ON THE SPEEDING CAR...

YOU'RE NOT GETTING AWAY SO EASILY, MALONNI!

HE'S RIGHT ON TOP OF US!

GOOD!

A TOUCH OF A SWITCH ON THE DASH-BOARD... AND...

TRAPPED! WHAT KIND OF A CAR IS THIS?

THOSE BARS ARE HIGH-TENSION STEEL. HE WON'T GET OUT OF THERE IN A HURRY! WE'VE CAPTURED THUNDERBOLT!

THE CAR ROARED ON AND ON... AND THEN TURNED OFF THE MAIN ROAD ALONG A RUTTED TRACK...

CASTLE CORTELL! BUT THIS PLACE IS A RUIN... NO ONE'S LIVED HERE FOR YEARS!

SAY, WHAT KIND OF A GLOOMY DUMP IS THIS, ANYWAY?

I LIVE HERE, MALONNI. ONE OR TWO ROOMS ARE QUITE HABITABLE. YOU'LL SEE!

WHAT ABOUT HIM? YOU DON'T KNOW HOW STRONG HE IS. HE MIGHT EVEN PULL THOSE BARS APART AND GET OUT.

I DON'T THINK SO. I'M JUST GOING TO PUT AN ELECTRIC CURRENT THROUGH THE BARS... ENOUGH POWER TO KILL ANYONE! FORTUNATELY FOR HIM THE ROOF IS INSULATED!

I WANT THE SECRET OF YOUR AMAZING POWER, THUNDERBOLT! TELL ME... AND I'LL GIVE YOU SAFE PASSAGE OUT OF HERE... AND ONE MILLION POUNDS IN GOLD!

REFUSE... AND YOU WILL DIE! THIS CASTLE HAS BEEN MINED! IN ONE HOUR IT WILL BE BLOWN TO SMITHEREENS AND YOU WITH IT! YOU HAVE YOUR CHOICE. WE'LL LEAVE YOU TO THINK IT OVER...

LEAVING THUNDERBOLT IN THE ELECTRIFIED CAGE, THE TWO MEN WALKED INTO THE CASTLE...

WELL, BOSS... WE'VE DONE IT! THUNDERBOLT IS SURE TO GIVE UP HIS SECRET...RATHER THAN BE BLOWN TO PIECES!

THERE'S NO NEED FOR YOU TO SOUND SO PLEASED WITH YOURSELF, MALONNI... YOU'VE OUTLIVED YOUR USEFULNESS!

WHAT—WHAT DO YOU MEAN?

THUNDERBOLT WILL TELL ME HIS SECRET... BUT HE WON'T GET A MILLION IN GOLD. I DON'T HAVE SUCH A SUM. NO...THE CASTLE WILL BE BLOWN UP...AND YOU AND THUNDERBOLT WITH IT!

THEN, WITH THUNDERBOLT'S POWER AT MY COMMAND...I'LL HOLD THE WHOLE WORLD TO RANSOM NO ONE WILL BE ABLE TO STOP ME...ANYTHING I WANT...I'LL TAKE!

OUT IN THE COURTYARD, THUNDERBOLT WAS MAKING HIS MOVE!

IF I CAN'T TOUCH THE BARS...THEN I'LL SMASH MY WAY OUT DOWNWARDS!

THE HUGE OAK, NAIL-STUDDED CASTLE DOORS WERE NO OBSTACLE TO THE SUPER STRENGTH OF THUNDERBOLT...

AAAARRH!

THUNDERBOLT! BUT—YOU COULDN'T ESCAPE. IT'S IMPOSSIBLE!

THE MAN SPRANG ACROSS TO THE BOOK-LINED WALL, HURRIEDLY PRESSING A BUTTON WHICH CAUSED THE WALL TO REVOLVE!

BUT I'M NOT FINISHED YET!

DON'T LET HIM GET AWAY, THUNDERBOLT! HE—HE WAS GOING TO KILL BOTH OF US AS SOON AS YOU'D TOLD HIM YOUR SECRET!

AFTER MAKING MALONNI COMFORTABLE, THE ONE-MAN POLICE FORCE BEGAN HIS SEARCH FOR HIS SINISTER ENEMY.

IF HE MAKES A RUN FOR IT...I'M BOUND TO SEE HIM UP HERE!

YOU WON'T GET AWAY IN THAT, CHUM! I'VE SEEN JUST ABOUT ALL THE TRICKS THAT CAR IS CAPABLE OF!

THUNDERBOLT SWOOPED DOWN...AND THE HEADLAMPS OF THE CAR SWUNG ASIDE...

NOT ALL THE TRICKS, THUNDERBOLT! HERE'S ONE YOU DIDN'T KNOW ABOUT...MACHINE-GUNS IN THE HEADLAMPS!

THUNDERBOLT LANDED...BETWEEN THE TWO STREAMS OF BULLETS!

UP YOU COME, CHUM!

NO! DON'T! PUT ME DOWN...I-I'LL DO A DEAL WITH YOU, THUNDERBOLT...

THE ONLY DEAL YOU'RE GOING TO DO...IS WITH THE POLICE... MY FRIEND!

AAAAGGGHHH!

HAVE YOU HAD ENOUGH? OR WOULD YOU LIKE TO MATCH YOURSELF AGAINST ME AGAIN?

NO...NO, PLEASE...DON'T TOUCH ME! I-I SURRENDER... I-I'M BEATEN...

FIVE MINUTES LATER...

IF YOU WANT TO CATCH TIGER MALONNI... AND HIS BOSS, YOU'LL FIND THEM AT A PHONE BOOTH NEAR CASTLE CORTELL. THEY'LL BE-ER-HANGING ON FOR YOU TO ARRIVE.... A PRESENT FROM THUNDERBOLT!

AT POOL STREET POLICE STATION, SERGEANT MEREDITH REPLACED THE RECEIVER WITH A LOOK OF AWE ON HIS FACE...

MARY...THUNDERBOLT'S CAPTURED TIGER MALONNI AND THE MAN MALONNI WAS WORKING FOR... SINGLEHANDED!

ISN'T HE AMAZING! IF ONLY WE HAD THE CHANCE TO MEET HIM...

THE END

BRR! WHAT A DAY TO HAVE TO GO OUT! BUT I PROMISED MY PALS I'D MEET THEM!

SUDDENLY...

SNOWBALL AWAY! HUR, HUR!

ULP! I'M UNDER ATTACK!

THUD

WOWIE! A DIRECT HIT!

SEEMS LIKE A GOOD TIME TO DISAPPEAR!

BLINK

SPLODGE

BUT...

UH? WH-WHERE'S SHE'S GONE?

SHE'S VANISHED!

PAH! I KNOW WHO SHE MUST BE — DISAPPEARING TRIX! BUT SHE CAN'T MAKE HER FOOTPRINTS DISAPPEAR!

WE CAN FOLLOW THEM!

Tin TEACHER

FOR THE LAST TIME... I'M NOT *QUEEN BOADICEA!* I'M THE COOK... SO, HOPPIT.'

I'VE GOT TO PUT FORWARD T-T'S CALENDAR DIAL TO 1982... OR WE WON'T HAVE ANY KITCHEN LEFT.'

YUK, YUK.' FANCY HIM THINKING YOU'RE BOADICEA.' WHAT A LAUGH.'

AH, GOT IT.' NOW I'LL TURN IT FORWARD TO 1982... *YEOW.' I'VE SLIPPED.'*

LEAD US, GREAT QUEEN.'

I'M OFF HOME.'

BLEEP.' WHERE AM I? AH.' I KNOW... I'M IN *ANGLO-SAXON ENGLAND.'* THE *VIKINGS* ARE INVADING US NOW.'

800 AD

BLEEP.' OH, KING ALFRED.' YOU'VE BURNT THE CAKES.'

K-KING ALFRED? WHO— *ME?* BUT I'M CYRIL SHORTBUCKET... SCHOOL PASTRY COOK.'

BLEEP.' NEVER MIND, YOUR HIGHNESS.' LEAVE THE CAKES.' DON YOUR WAR HELMET.' GRAB YOUR BATTLE-AXE AND DRIVE OFF THE VIKINGS.'

DONG

KITCHEN

BLEEP.' FORWARD, ALFRED THE GREAT.' TO BATTLE.'

PHEW.' ONE GOOD THING... THERE AREN'T ANY VIKINGS ABOUT NOW.'

HE'S GONE BARMY.'

BLEEP.' LOOK, ALFRED.' *VIKINGS.'* WAITING TO AMBUSH YOUR ARMY.' I CAN SEE THE HORNS ON THEIR HELMETS BEHIND YON WALL.'

EH?

OH, *NO.'* HE THINKS OUR CYCLE HANDLEBARS ARE VIKING HELMETS.'

BLEEP.' CHAARGE.' DOWN WITH THE VIKINGS.'

BLEEP.' HAVE AT THEE.' SAXONS FOR EVER.'

I'M OFF.'

CLANG

TINKLE TINKLE

CRASH

PSSS.'

IT'S ALL BEETLE'S FAULT FOR MESSING ABOUT WITH T-T'S DATE-SELECTOR-DIAL.'

89

CHOCS. ICES etc.

NO PARKING

THIS VEHICLE HAS BEEN DUMPED

SNORE

SHORTLY...

IT'LL TAKE HOURS TO MEND.

CITY DUMP

SNORE

THAT TRAFFIC WARDEN'S GONE *TOO FAR!* IT'S TIME TO BRING IN MY *ULTIMATE WEAPON!*

SNORE

...GOLIATH! SUPER FERRET!

SNORE

MEANWHILE, IN THE HIGH STREET...

DIRECTING TRAFFIC IS A JOB I REALLY ENJOY.

SCREEECH

A JOB I'M REALLY GOOD AT — SNIFF.

Fried BREAD

I DON'T SEE WHAT GOLIATH CAN DO, FRED?

SNORE

OH, NO? JUST WATCH *THIS* THEN.

ER... DON'T CRY, LITTLE GIRL... FATHER XMAS WILL SOON BE HERE FOR OUR PARTY...

VILLAGE HALL

BUT...

MY CAR'S STUCK IN A SNOWDRIFT! I CAN'T SHIFT IT!

WAIT... PERHAPS THERE'S A TOY PLASTIC SPADE AMONG THE XMAS PRESENTS!

WHAT'S THIS OLD BOX DOING IN HERE? I'LL GET RID OF IT...

THERE'S A SINK PLUNGER IN IT— MUST BE A PRESENT FOR THE PLUMBER'S SON!

CLICK

THUNK

SPROINN GGG

CLICK CLICK CLICK

EEK! DON'T... GO.. UP.. WITHOUT ME!

WHIRRRRR

Helpful HETTIE

MY MUM SAYS I CAN'T HAVE ANY TEA UNTIL I'VE CLEARED ALL MY TOYS AWAY!

DON'T SHED A TEAR, HELPFUL HETTIE'S HERE!

JUST OPEN THE CUPBOARD DOOR AND IN EVERYTHING GOES!

PANT! THERE YOU ARE, ALL SAFELY PUT AWAY IN NO TIME AT ALL! PUFF!

THANKS, HETTIE!

SLAM

WELL DONE, HETTIE! I'LL JUST PUT HIS COWBOY HAT AWAY AND THEN WE'LL HAVE TEA!

ERK! I HADN'T THOUGHT ABOUT WHAT WOULD HAPPEN WHEN THE DOOR WAS OPENED!

CRASH!

CRACK!

THUD

RATTLE

103

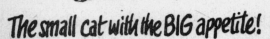

107

AFTER THAT, BERTIE DECIDED IT WAS SAFER ON THE FARM...

HI! FARMER CRABFACE! OI WANT A WORD WITH EE!

OI WANT MOI WHEELBARROW BACK WHICH EE BORROWED SIX MONTHS AGO!

HUMPH! YOU'LL FIND IT IN THE BARN!

TEE, HEE! BERTIE'LL FIND MORE THAN HIS WHEELBARROW IN THERE! SNIGGER!

BELLOW!

HA, HA! THAT DON'T LOOK MUCH LIKE A WHEELBARROW, BERTIE! HEH, HEH, HEH!

HELP!

SNORT!

THIS IS THE LAST STRAW!

SNORT!

CHALKY

CHALKY BOUGHT SOME SWEETS WITH THE REWARD MONEY...

YUMMY! LET'S GET EATING THESE SWEETS!

HAND OVER THOSE SWEETS!

GULP! BANDITS!

RUN!

THEY'LL CATCH US! THEY'RE BIGGER THAN US!

THESE TRACKS WILL FOOL THEM!

HERE THEY COME!

THEY'LL FOLLOW THE TRACKS!

HUH! CHALKY'S UP TO HIS TRICKS AGAIN!

BAH! THEY'RE STILL AFTER US!

GULP! WHO'S HE?

IT'S ONLY ANOTHER OF CHALKY'S DRAWINGS!

BURST THAT BAG WHEN I GIVE THE WORD..!

BANG

GULP! THAT'S NO DRAWING! HE'S SHOOTING AT US!

HO, HO! THAT CHALK DUST I THREW AND THE BANG OF THE BAG BURSTING REALLY FOOLED THEM!

PANIC

NOW WE CAN EAT OUR SWEETS! THEY'RE SAFE IN MY POCKET!

CONSTERNATION STREET

IVOR LOTT and TONY BROKE

GOSH! I'M LATE FOR SCHOOL AGAIN... THE POOR OLD WATCH MUM BOUGHT IN A **JUMBLE SALE** HAS LET ME DOWN AS USUAL!

MINUTES LATER...

TONY WASN'T IN CLASS AT THE **STROKE OF NINE** SO NOW HE'S GETTING **NINE STROKES** TO REMIND HIM TO BE MORE **PUNCTUAL!**

THWACK! THWACK!

YEEEOWL!

AFTER SCHOOL...

DON'T KNOW WHY YOU LAUGHED WHILE I WAS BEING WHACKED ...ANYONE CAN BE **LATE** FOR SCHOOL, YOU KNOW!

NOT ME! NOT EVER!

AND HERE COMES THE **REASON** WHY!

WHAT IS IT? A **MISSILE?**

TONY SOON HAD HIS ANSWER...

PATER'S HAVING AN EXACT REPLICA OF **BIG BEN** PLACED OUTSIDE **MY** BEDROOM WINDOW... WE'RE CALLING IT **BIG BOB!**

WOW! IT MUST BE THE WORLD'S BIGGEST **ALARM CLOCK!**

THAT NIGHT...

HO HUM! NOW FOR A NICE **PEACEFUL** NIGHT'S SLEEP!

JUST THEN...

OH, BOY! LISTEN TO THAT **LOVELY** ROW... IT CAN'T FAIL TO WAKE ME UP IN THE MORNING!

DONG! DONG! DONG!

BUT, AN HOUR LATER...

OH, NO! I FORGOT BIG BOB CHIMED **EVERY HOUR** ON THE **HOUR!**

DONG! DONG! DONG!

AN HOUR LATER...

DONG! DONG! DONG!

AT THIS RATE THE WRETCHED CLOCK CAN'T FAIL TO **KEEP ME AWAKE** ALL NIGHT EITHER!

NEXT MORNING...

Y-A-W-N! I DIDN'T GET A **WINK** OF SLEEP!

NEVER MIND, SIR... **WE'LL DRESS YOU!**

RENT-A-GHOST Ltd.

117

119

THE SCARECROW DICE GAME

FOR ANY NUMBER OF PLAYERS

YOU WILL NEED A DICE TO PLAY THIS GAME AND EACH PLAYER WILL NEED A PENCIL AND SOME PAPER. TURNS ARE TAKEN TO THROW THE DICE; IF THE THROWER ROLLS A **ONE** HE GETS A BODY AND DRAWS IT ON HIS PAPER. **TWO** IS A HEAD—**THREE** IS A HAT—**FOUR** IS A LEFT ARM—**FIVE** A RIGHT ARM AND **SIX** IS THE STICK THAT SUPPORTS HIM. THE FIRST TO COMPLETE THREE SCARECROWS IS THE WINNER!

THIS IS HOW YOU DRAW HIM!

I'M GOING TO THE BIG FOOTBALL MATCH TODAY!... BRR! IT LOOKS COLD OUT THERE!

I'LL BE WARM ENOUGH IF I WRAP UP WELL

I'M SUPPOSED TO BE MEETING MY PALS, BUT WHERE ARE THEY?

AH! THERE THEY ARE!

HI, YOU TWO! I DIDN'T RECOGNISE YOU TILL I USED MY X-RAY SPECS!

HELLO, RAY! BANG ON TIME!

READERS! WITHOUT USING X-RAY SPECS, CAN YOU SPOT RAY IN THE CROWD?

GUMS IS REALLY **MAD** BECAUSE WE GOT AWAY!

HE'LL **RUIN** THE POWER BOAT RACE!

UNLESS...

HUH! YOU GOT AN IDEA, BLUEY?

AND SO...

HMM! SEEMS LIKE A GOOD PLAN, BLUEY, SO YOU CAN BORROW THE BALLOON!

THANKS, CAPTAIN!

HMM! IT'S GONE **QUIET!**

THEN...

THUD

OOF! ME NUT!

SNARL! I'LL TEACH YOU TO CHUCK **SANDBAGS** AT ME!

READY WITH THE ROPE, DIGGER?

READY, BLUEY!

SNAP